Owen Kelly has been a

enough to be the subject of a BBC television documentary, *Now and Then*. His credits include: hundreds of short stories for BBC Radio 4, Radio Ulster, Radio Foyle and the World Service; some 200 editions of *Kelly's Fancy* and two series of *Not Famous But Great* for BBC Radio Ulster; two radio dramas and an arts documentary; two long-running columns for the *Irish News* — 'Kelly's World' and 'The Saturday Column' — and a literary column, 'On The Page'. Owen has also written two volumes of autobiography (*Tales Out Of School* and *Hens' Teeth*) and *Kelly's Fancy*, a collection of short pieces drawn from his newspaper, radio and magazine work. He is the author of the bestselling *Essential Norn Irish: Yer Man's A to Z Guide to Everyday Banter*, and *Kelly's World*, which are both published by The Brehon Press. Owen currently lives in Belfast.

By the same author

Kelly's World
Essential Norn Irish:
Yer Man's A to Z Guide to Everyday Banter
Tales Out Of School
Hens' Teeth
Kelly's Fancy

KELLY'S COUNTRY

KELLY'S COUNTRY

Tales from the Farm Gate

OWEN KELLY

THE BREHON PRESS
BELFAST

Published 2006 by
The Brehon Press Ltd
1A Bryson Street
Belfast BT5 4ES,
Northern Ireland

Originally published in 2005
as *Those Were the Days: Short Stories from Ballinascreen*
by the Ballinascreen Historical Society

ISBN: 1 905474 05 9

Printed and bound by J.H. Haynes & Co Ltd, Sparkford

for my grandchildren
Katie, Rosie, Maeve, Callum, Daniel and Cormac

Contents

The Smell of Money *13*
By Hook or By Crook *16*
Bog-trotting *19*
A Needle in a Haystack *22*
The Mason *25*
The Handyman *28*
She Put Her Shirt on Him *31*
The Legend of the Cow-catcher *34*
It Would Make a Cat Laugh ... *37*
Stock Comes First *40*
Pets *43*
Rat Race *46*
Turfed Out *49*
Woodcutter, Spare That Tree *52*
Calling a Spade a Spade? *55*
The Turf-Shed *58*
Farmyards Now and Then *61*
Farm Gate? What Farm Gate? *64*

Having Your Chips *67*
Clever Bees *70*
Bread *73*
A Bread and Butter Issue *76*
The Boiler Suit *79*
To Cap It All *82*
Of Barns and Raffles *85*
Peter Dog One *88*
The Social Whirl *91*
New Lamps for Old *94*
Rural Humour *97*
The Last Sixpence *100*
Horsepower or Manpower? *103*
Sauce for the Goose *106*
As Sure as Eggs *109*
Duck! *112*
The Labourer is Worthy
of His Hire? *115*
Rustling *118*
Thatching *121*

Keep it in the Family! *124*
Gathering in the ... Sheaves? *127*
Gold in Them Thar Hills *130*
The Fox Runs Long ... *133*
Summertime
— and the Duties were Easy *136*
Money for Old Rope *139*

The Smell of Money

When you look at a piece of snowy Irish linen it's hard to square it with its less than glamorous origins. Getting the flax out of the ground, after a season of anxiously watching it for signs of blight, was the easiest part of the lengthy process that began with the oily seed and ended with the brilliant tablecloth.

The stalk had to be separated from the fibre and the first stage of that process will not be easily forgotten by those who had anything to do with it. It had to be soaked for fourteen nights, head down in a flax dam, otherwise a lint dam. Large stones helped it to sink and people got on with something else while nature took her course and softened the stuff.

Flax had its own vocabulary. A sheaf was a beet, the seed was measured in bushels and pecks (a term now used only in body-building) and the softening process was retting — not rotting — just for contrariness.

Another of the many forms of cussedness associated with flax was the fact that, regardless of what day of the week it was put in the dam — and even taking account of the sacred fourteen nights, which also, you will note, gave it a bit of a day extra at both ends of the process, making it fifteen days in all — it only ever seemed to be ready for taking out of the dam on a Sunday. It may have rained for the previous two weeks, but on the Sunday you could count on the sun splitting the stones.

None of this would have mattered all that much except for the stench. The countryside reeked of it and people got so used to it they hardly noticed but once you handled the stuff — and it was a hands-on process, because you had to get into the dam and manhandle the sodden beets out — the smell seemed to work its way into every pore. And stay there.

You could bathe, wash, scrub all you liked and douse yourself in all the perfumes of Arabia, as Lady Macbeth put it, but just as in her ladyship's case, the effect was only superficial. It wore off, of course, but rarely in time for the Sunday night dance, or if it did, a few turns round the floor revived it.

'What's that smell?' a visiting young lady enquired of her dance partner one stuffy August Sunday night in the Hib. Hall on Tonagh Hill.

'Money,' he said, quick as a flash. And it proved to be a very good chat-up line indeed.

By Hook or By Crook

Terence Patrick Dolan's *Dictionary of Hiberno-English* fell open, in the way that might have happened with certain passages from say *Lady Chatterley's Lover*, at the word 'bool'. It instantly beamed me back in time as efficiently as that gadget from *Star Trek*. Though he defines it as the handle of a bucket, we know rather better, you and I.

The bool was a vital component in the state-of-the-art cooking equipment that preceded the Stanley 9, that preceded the Rayburn, that preceded, well, you know what preceded what in the house our grandfathers built. The crane-crook swivelled the pot over the open fire, a double-ended hook linked it up and down the central vertical holed bar and the bool, a handle to be sure but collapsible, hooked into either side of the pot.

The farmer's wife knew to a nicety exactly how high or low the pot should hang, though much of the secret lay in the strength of the fire. The exception was the oven pot, flat at both bottom and top. A layer of coals on the lid ensured even baking from above and below.

Of course, the pots and the griddle needed constant supervision, the fire needed constant topping-up and the cooking, or baking, processes were long drawn-out and sometimes ran past the daylight hours into the night, when the ceiliers drew their chairs round the fire with their legs stretched towards the blaze, complicating the movements of the cook/baker. One farm wife in our parish once thought to shorten the ceili night by letting the fire die down. This was not lost on one of the company, a sarcastic man who felt his sarcasm should be evenly divided and that night she had drawn the short straw. He asked what she was cooking. She snappily replied that it was a chicken. He picked up a spare pair of bools, lifted the lid of the pot and viewed the tepid contents.

'Let it out,' he commanded, 'or it'll die of a founder.'

Fortunately, in the interests of neighbourliness, he didn't experience another function of the bools, for they were often used by no-nonsense farm wives to drive away wandering animals, tinkers or other undesirables. Which brings me, rather neatly, to a bit of 19th century Irish-American slang for policemen. Professor Dolan wonders in his dictionary about how 'booly-dogs' came to be used in this connection. While I never actually saw a farmer's wife enforcing law and order with a swinging pair of bools, there were enough tales of it around in my youth to visualise their transition to the streets of New York, complete with blue uniform and truncheon.

Some, I feel sure, would have passed the medical with ease.

Bog-trotting

We were heading towards Limerick with time on our hands when I spotted the sign for trips on the Blackwater Bog, so I bought tickets for the mini-train and settled back to enjoy the trip. At a certain point on the vast prairie of stripped bog the train coasted to a halt and the guide suggested we get out and try our hands at turf-cutting.

'This is your chance,' whispered Herself. 'You're from turf country. Get out and have a go.'

'It's because I'm from turf country,' I hissed back, 'that I'm staying exactly where I am.'

I've never cut turf but I've been there when it happened. I've holed, footed and wheeled them, stacked them and even burned them but I've only ever been a spectator at the sharp end of the operation. So, when a volunteer stood up to a ripple of applause I settled back to watch his efforts with the keenest interest.

His trainers were gleaming white, fresh out of their box; his jeans had that pure blueness that goes only with brand-newness and the snowy tee-shirt clearly stated that here was a pumper of iron. Weights, though, are one thing and a turf-spade is something else and before he was many minutes older the clothes had lost their newness, the children had ceased to cheer him on, his wife had opened her newspaper and something in her posture suggested a desire for the train to move on leaving him behind. Turf-cutting is an activity that separates the men from the boys.

Some things have changed. I encountered a quartet of turf cutters in recent years and they were wearing work-gloves, a sensible precaution which nonetheless would have had previous generations of turf cutters spinning in their graves. The ancient, sacred and inefficient custom of bringing all the makings of a meal to the turf bank, fetching water and lighting fires had given way to sizeable lunch boxes — surplus Victory Assorted tins — and sensible flasks. The work, though, hadn't changed a bit. I could see that at a glance.

'Where are you from?' one of them asked.

'Down there,' I said, pointing down the valley to where I was born, bred and buttered.

He studied my well-scuffed walking boots and the rucksack, stained with unidentifiable substances from nearly every mountain in the Sperrins.

'It must have been a long time ago,' he said. Four knowing laughs sounded on cue, and, as one man, they went back to work. I've puzzled over that enigmatic remark many a time since, I can tell you.

A Needle in a Haystack

A man in our townland once found a needle in a haystack. Needles in haystacks are not supposed to be found. It's a metaphor for the impossible. Nonetheless he did it. It was a packing needle, which made discovery marginally easier, I suppose, because it's bigger than the conventional needle, maybe six inches long, as thick as a six-inch nail and flattened and curved at the business end.

Its use was for sewing cord in the tops of potato sacks, corn bags and grass-seed bags. One local bachelor patched the seat of his trousers with one, which wasn't a work of art but then neither was he. Our man found the packing needle by accident, in the way you might find a small screw on the floor if you walk around in your socks.

He was pulling hay for fodder from the side of a stack when a neighbour stopped to pass the time of day and our man sat into the dent in the stack. That's when he made the discovery. He came out of the improvised seat like something out of Cape Canaveral, calling upon a range of deities, some heathen, some not, to come to his aid. The neighbour yanked the thing out of his seating arrangements but you can't keep a thing like that secret — there was, after all, an eyewitness — and the word spread like wildfire.

Questions were asked in order of importance. How did the needle get in the haystack? What held it so firmly that it didn't slide further in when his weight hit it? Was he hurt? You can see the sufferer's relative unimportance in practical terms here.

The needle was rusty and the wound became infected. He wouldn't seek professional help because two of the three local doctors were women and naturally would never have seen the like before, which might, on reflection, be true. The male doctor was on holiday so the sufferer suffered and poulticed until nature took its course and cured him, thus proving what a famous medical teacher once said, that most things get better by themselves, in fact most things are better by morning.

Our man had been about to fodder — 'fother' in the local patois — outlying cattle and I remembered all this when I came across the German word 'drachenfutter'. It seems when a German goes out for a few pints, he often brings home a box of chocolates as drachenfutter, which means dragon-fodder. You may care to reflect on this valuable, insightful information.

The Mason

When I was a small boy — and despite all appearances to the contrary, I was at one time — I knew a man who built cottages at £8 a time. And that included thatching. I didn't know that at the time but many years later another builder told me. It must have been in the early days of the 20th century, what my grandmother would have called the 'chape times'. He was a stone mason by trade. 'Mason by trade, messin' by nature,' he used to say. He was anticipating modern slang by half a century and more.

His name was Neil Mullan and he was a droll character indeed. He was welcome wherever he went for his social skills almost as much as for his craftsmanship. He was a fine storyteller when the day's work was done. You see, he usually stayed in the houses he was working at. I particularly remember his reworking of an old Irish tale about the pitfalls of gossip. He gave flesh and blood, a name and a contemporary setting to the story of the man who took to his bed with a bad fit of coughing. Word spread that he had swallowed a crow.

One neighbour told another and by nightfall the number of crows had grown to seven. Seven is a mystical kind of a number in Irish mythology. The whole district was in a fine state of excitement. Everybody was anticipating a wake. They were all rehearsing the nice things they'd say about him as soon as the crows got the better of him. The next morning the man was seen out working in one of his fields and everybody was disappointed. 'What's all this blether about crows?' the man demanded crossly. 'I coughed up something as black as a crow, that's all. It was only a bit of burnt scone. That woman's baking will be the death of me yet.'

The reference to baking is significant because Neil had been an eligible bachelor in his younger days, a man with a steady trade. Farmers with eligible daughters to dispose of made him welcome because it was a good chance for them to show off their culinary skills. When one farmer engaged him to build a barn he spent far too much time extolling the virtues of his three daughters. This meant he was holding up the work and delaying Neil's departure to the next job. Neil brought the eulogy to an end.

'You've convinced me,' he told the proud father politely. 'I'll take two.'

He took none of the many offers and was found dead of natural causes in his lonely bed sixty years or so ago. I don't imagine many of his cottages are now standing but the important thing is that he is remembered in those parts and they tell his stories still. That's maybe a better monument.

The Handyman

The chief difference between a handyman and a handy woman in rural life was that the handy woman delivered babies, which was about the only thing handymen didn't do. The handyman could make a door and hang it, build a house or a henhouse, or turn his hand to painting and decorating, or a bit of roofing, with equal ease.

He might have served his time to a trade or he just might have picked up bits and pieces of skills as he went along. The results weren't always perfect. When they weren't they often passed into folklore.

One Ballinascreen farmer's wife engaged a local handyman to do up her kitchen. Since she and her husband had no children the long table that stood against the back wall was rarely pulled out, except at the threshing or on a similar occasion. At all other times she and her husband took their meals at one end of it.

The fashion at the time was to do the lower half of the walls one colour, the upper half a different shade and mark the division of the two with a strip of border paper. The entire refurbishment was carried out as per contract, including the walls, but for some time afterwards she had a vague feeling that all wasn't well. She had the impression, for example, that the tea in her cup, instead of being level as the laws of physics require, seemed to lie at a slant. The same applied to the milk in the jug and the soup in the bowls but she hesitated to mention these developments to her husband.

He hadn't noticed anything out of the ordinary. He was likely to tell her she was cracked, a popular local expression of the time and place, and retreat once more into the quiet landscape of his own mind where he contemplated more important issues such as drainage, cattle prices, the weather and the hundred and one topics that preoccupied a single-handed farmer.

The mystery was solved when the thresher came, the table was pulled out into the middle of the floor and opened out fully to feed the workers. The neighbouring girl who came in to help with the catering accidentally manhandled the table back into its place the wrong way round.

This revealed the fact that the new border paper was running off by a couple of inches. The handyman had cunningly offset this discrepancy by sawing two inches off the two table-legs at one end. The farmer's wife, to her credit, did nothing about it. She was so relieved, you see, to discover that she wasn't cracking up after all.

She Put Her Shirt on Him

There were elaborate Christmas rituals surrounding rural courtship in the long-ago involving brides-to-be with priceless potential, such as a bit of adjoining land that was likely to come their way and consequently into the clutches of a husband. These young women were a privileged minority, though. The vast majority had to develop other attractions.

One such lady in our parish had her eye on a local man, who shall we say, didn't have his eye on her. She decided to give him a Christmas present. This was a serious declaration of intent for in those days Christmas gift-giving was a long way from the epidemic proportions of the present day.

She decided to make him a shirt. Now there are certain basic requirements for a project of this sort. A few statistics might come in handy. The neck size, for example, would be useful to know. Chest measurements would be a useful pointer. Sleeve length would add to the overall picture.

She knew none of these things and she could hardly ask. It wasn't just a case of spoiling the surprise, because such romantic considerations hadn't been invented then; it would also show her hand too soon.

She had one or two other handicaps to overcome. Shirt-making even in the machine age is a skilled business and her needlework skills didn't extend far beyond knowing that the thread went into the blunter end of the needle. She acquired some guidance by furtive inspection of her father's Sunday shirt. He had to be kept in the dark, too.

She did finish the shirt. She gave it to her dream man, who by chance called at the house the day before Christmas Eve. She persuaded him, legend doesn't specify how, to step into a room off the kitchen and try it on.

When he finally emerged he looked curiously deformed. One sleeve barely passed his elbow, the other covered his hand. It was significantly shorter at the front than at the back. There was an interesting ripple effect across the chest. It was the collar, though, that completed the Quasimodo effect. The buttons ran across the left shoulder so that he looked like a cross between Dr Kildare and something out of Hans Christian Andersen.

The dream died there. You couldn't keep a thing like that secret in the country in those days and word of the bizarre Christmas gift was out before noon on Christmas Eve. One neighbour, risking life and limb, for the man in question was a well-made chap, enquired what he thought of the shirt. He summed up her sartorial efforts in five words.

'It had buttons on it,' he said.

The Legend of the Cow-catcher

The fact that English railway companies have to set aside hundreds of millions for compensation underlines the destiny of railways since, as the schoolboy howler puts it, 'Stephenson invested steam'. The iron road was destined to be a focus for complaints, the butt of comedians and a source of compensation from the day the first locomotive trundled down the track at twenty miles an hour, prompting gloomy prophecies from the medical profession that the human frame couldn't withstand such meteoric speeds.

Our own local branch line was never profitable. It ended at the edge of Draperstown and my personal recollections amount to being sent there to collect our school's allocation of coal on one occasion and, later, to spending a freezing winter day helping to re-sort five tons of our potatoes rejected at Belfast docks by a particularly bloody-minded inspector.

There were lighter moments, though they were long before my time, and my father once wryly recounted a local legend about a devious farmer, a missing cow and, as the newspapers of the time used to put it so grandly, its sequel in court. One of the farmer's cows went missing and a local prankster put it in his head that the train was responsible. The land ran along the line, after all.

The joker painted a graphic word picture of American trains with cow-catchers on the front — he had travelled a bit and seen a Western or two — and planted the idea that even as he spoke the cow was being converted into steaks and sausages in faraway Belfast. The farmer promptly took an action against the railway company and decided to argue his own case.

The railway company, fully realising that if they weren't careful it could be the beginning of a flood of claims against an already unprofitable line, contested the case. It eventually came to court before a judge who detested the idea of people arguing their own cases, but he disliked the railway company's lawyer even more and, more or less, argued the farmer's case for him, giving him words like issue (calves) and provenance (milk) to play about with, so that the missing animal began to sound like a worthy mate for the Brown Bull of Cooley.

Finally he awarded £10, £8 for the animal (it was the 1930s, after all) and another £2 for the big words. The railway company's lawyer stopped the farmer on the way out and told him he hadn't done as well as he thought, for he had been authorised to settle out of court for £12. The farmer looked down at his boots — black, Sunday models — and up at some interesting architectural feature on the courthouse roof. Finally he spoke.

'It was all right,' he said. 'She came home herself three days later.'

It Would Make a Cat Laugh ...

Figures show that the cost of maintaining a cosseted cat comes out at just under £10,000 over its lifetime. Dogs are a bit pricier, at £13,000. Mind you, injections of one sort or another account for £1,560 of this total in each case, insurance costs about the same and boarding fees a shade over £1,400. I read these statistics with mind agape, looked at our own useless and barely decorative moggie industriously sleeping under the radiator and too thick to know it wasn't on, then I opened the window and listened to the sound of my father's generation of farmers whirling like dervishes in their graves. Maybe it was only a trick of the wind.

We had two cats on the strength of the farm.

They didn't have names. They were known as the black cat and the other cat. The black cat was in charge of the barn where the bags of corn were stacked in rows with narrow aisles between them. They drew mice like a magnet and she slew them with silent, ferocious efficiency. She showed up for the morning and evening milking, consumed the obligatory saucer of milk and stalked off, contemptuous of all creatures great and small.

The other cat was a big, grey amiable creature who thought she was a dog. She accompanied the dog to the thresher to assist in the annihilation of the rats that had hibernated in the corn stacks. The dog was a ham actor and made a three act play out of each kill. The cat gave each rat a head start and then took off like something out of a Tom and Jerry cartoon. The rodent had no chance.

Both cats died within days of each other, victims of a cat flu that swept the district clear of cats. Vets? For cats? Anybody simple-minded enough to even suggest such a thing would never be allowed to forget it. They'd be pointed out and sniggered at in Draperstown fair for years after it.

Kittens imported from outside the district died like flies during the epidemic and the mice raced in March Hare madness through the barns and store houses, jeering at mechanical traps.

One kitten weathered the storm but only after intensive medication. This consisted entirely of Apros crushed in warm milk and administered with a spoon — total outlay probably four pence, old money. One day it got out of the box beside the range, where it had lived since its arrival, and took a turn round the yard. The restoration of law and order in the barn was about to begin.

Stock Comes First

A curate in our parish in the old days told me about a previous posting, and one farmer who, on the plus side, had a particularly clever dog and on the minus side, a social-climbing wife with little sympathy for the round-the-clock demands of farming.

One blazing summer day she announced that some of her well-heeled city friends were coming to lunch and he was to be cleaned up in his Sunday best from noon onwards and generally look decorative.

He said one of the cows out in the meadow was due to calve and he had to keep an eye on her. This cut no ice with his wife, so you can see right away what he was up against. Come the middle of the day he was hanging round his own kitchen, sweltering in his suit. There are few more uncomfortable spectacles than a farmer trussed up in a suit in his own house when the sun's splitting the stones.

The guests came and so did lunch and small talk, not one word of which was of any interest to our man, concerned for his expectant cow. From where he sat, cornered, he had a good view of the yard, the gate and the milk-house and as he studied this vista longingly he caught two or six warning looks from his wife. The dog took to racing out the gate and racing back, peering round the corner of the milk-house and generally being unsettled. Finally he came to the back door, which was open, and barked. And barked. And barked.

The wife chased him. He made another foray out the gate, then he did the unthinkable. He came right into the sitting room, grabbed the farmer's jacket in his teeth and tried to drag him out. The visitors thought this cute. The farmer thought it alarming. The wife thought it outrageous, expelled the dog and shut all doors.

From his uncomfortable vantage point the farmer saw the dog go into the milk-house and emerge seconds later with milk dripping from his tail. Then he raced once more out of the yard, only to return minutes later, driving the cow before him. Bringing up the rear and sucking his milk-soaked tail wobbled the newborn calf.

You can make what you like of that story. You're not suggesting that a man of the cloth would make up a tale like that?

Pets

An occasional theme on farming programmes has been farm animals as pets — sheep mostly, though there are exceptions. The farmers I know are unsentimental about their stock and take the 'no-reasonable-offer-refused' stance, though a poteen-maker of some distinction once told me of an incident that might have tended to prove otherwise.

By the nature of his profession he was often out and about on the farther flung borders of Ballinascreen when others were in bed, and one bright moonlit winter night he observed one neighbour in hot pursuit of another. The pursuer was handicapped by three days on the tear and the one in front was handicapped by a full, writhing woodbale on his back. The pursuer thought the bale was full of pups for drowning and he dearly wanted one, for the woodbale carrier was a sheepdog breeder of repute.

Just as he caught up, a dog put its head out of the bale and called him an offensive name, which not only stopped him in his tracks but sobered him completely and forever. The poteen-maker continued to follow the bale-carrier along the mountain track, over the stream, up the hill on the other side, all the way home. From there he pieced the whole story together.

The bale-carrier lived on one side of the valley, his mother, a cantankerous smallholder, on the other. The snow of 1947 had been deep and long-lasting and she had brought her four bullocks into her house, a ramshackle room and kitchen affair with a loft-ladder. She wisely retreated to the loft with a few provisions, for before long the bullocks had knocked down the ladder and trampled it into matchwood, leaving her marooned.

On the second day of the thaw the son turned up, carrying his woolbale, for it was his equivalent of a pickup truck. He carried everything from a few turf to an ailing sheep in it. He had to jump for his life when he opened the door and the four thirst-crazed bullocks stampeded out.

When he stepped into the malodorous wreckage his mother peered at him from the loft entrance, her hair in a halo of rats' tails round her grimy face and the last crust of her rations clutched in a grubby fist. She was unable to walk and he decided to move her to his own house after nightfall by the only transport available to him.

It was she, not a dog, that called their pursuer's parentage into question but in his fuddled state he didn't know that. Still, he never touched another drop and became a power in the land with all the time and money he saved and the poteen-maker had a fine story to tell at wakes for years afterwards. The Lord really does move in mysterious ways — especially among farming folk.

Rat Race

Research has shown that rats raised in a laboratory are less developed socially than sewer rats whose environment is richer. Richer? In a sewer? The mind boggles. I could name, without difficulty, a score of farmers with a lot to say on that subject, most of it unprintable.

'Any man that meets a rat,' a neighbour once proclaimed in our kitchen, 'should kill it at once, for if it's not going to do harm, it's coming from it.' That's the cleaned up version of his opinion. It underlines the divergence between science and agriculture.

Years ago I read that a company in Connecticut claimed rats could be trained to pack pills and they were better at it than people. I hope that the rodents were trained to operate levers that did the actual work. Not even a deranged person would willingly put a pill in their innards that had been packed by a rat-packer.

Of course, if childhood legend is to be believed, rats exhibited remarkable intelligence. They were allegedly adept at stealing potatoes in teams of three. One lay on its back, so the legend ran, holding the spud between all four paws, while number two pulled and number three shoved. Not a very likely tale, all things considered, since they were much more likely to gnaw — 'scobe' in the local dialect — the spuds in the store.

For these and assorted other reasons, they were farm enemy number one and they certainly weren't smart enough to change their habitat, spending their winters in the bases of the cornstacks and meeting annihilation when the thresher came in the spring. Threshing was a co-operative effort, and the farmers brought their dogs, which expectantly circled the rapidly shrinking stacks, waiting for the rats to begin their futile flight for the hedgerows.

Scores were kept, for a dog's ratting skills were highly prized. There were too many hands at one threshing and one farmer — we'll call him Murphy — tall, lean and surplus to requirements, armed himself with a long sally rod and slew a number with devastating accuracy. At the meal afterwards the local wag announced the scores.

'John McGurk's collie, five,' he said, 'Joe McEldowney's dog, seven. Mrs Murphy's hound, nine.'

There was no prize, apart from the guffaws of laughter. Nor, come to think of it, for Jimmy Cagney, either, who sadly told an awards ceremony in Hollywood that he had never once, in life or on screen, ever uttered the words forever associated with him, 'You dirty rat, you.'

Turfed Out

Turf-cutting, apart from its labour intensive, backbreaking and inefficient dimensions, was an operation invariably complicated by the weather, especially bad weather. You only had to say 'turf' even in the middle of a heat wave and a jesting deity would open the heavens and send down a deluge.

You won turf — that was the official expression — or you lost them. I was present at one such loss-making operation, when I was sent, on the morrowing principle — the exchange of labour between farmers — to assist a neighbour. He had a labourer called Frank on a kind of retainer and such was the nature of the employer-employee relations you would hardly know which was which, the labourer being as likely to cuss out or issue orders to his boss as the other way round.

He got into the back of the van, sat on a rolled-up raincoat and we set off in a downpour to foot the turf, on the optimistic premise that the rain might stop. The mountain was deserted when we arrived, everybody else wisely stayed at home and when our employer stepped out to test the land he sank up to his boot-tops. This annoyed Frank who said if he was drowned he — I didn't count — would have to walk home. He reminded the farmer he had won no turf the year before, would win none in the current year nor in the year to come. He also told him he was a right eejit. The eejit announced that he was going home to change into dry socks and boots.

When my colleague got out of the van dragging the raincoat he discovered it wasn't his own disreputable rag but our employer's Sunday best, now stained with unidentifiable substances from the floor of the van and resembling a relief map of some lost continent. We attempted a species of dry-cleaning operation while the owner was away, spreading the coat out on the heather and lighting a fire by rifling a nearby stack of dry turf. As we waited for miracles the culprit led me away over the bog to see the purest spring water in Ireland — a tiny well of such crystal purity it seemed empty. He was so proud of the water you'd have thought he made it himself.

In our absence the fire spread and consumed all but the inner metal core of the belt buckle and the buttons. We had barely scattered the ashes when the owner returned, studied the weather and the ground and called off the operation. He had also brought the culprit's disreputable rag and admonished him for being so foolish as to head off to the turf without a coat.

'Ah,' said the miscreant, uncharacteristically civil, 'you shouldn't have bothered. Sure fellas going about in vans don't need coats.'

Two out of the three of us knew the truth of that.

Woodcutter, Spare That Tree

Our Stanley 9 range was a serious consumer of fuel. It went through turf like the proverbial hot knife through butter, so the supply had to be supplemented from other sources. Another voracious consumer was the potato boiler which boiled the spuds in large quantities that would be mixed with crushed corn and meal to augment the cattle's winter feed.

We were lucky in one sense in that we had a more than adequate supply of timber on the farm. A belt of mature trees grew along the riverbank that marked one boundary of the land. We, and specifically I mean me, were unlucky in that the only method of cutting them down was with a crosscut saw. I think it must have come under the heading of light duties, or maybe my memory is selective, but I don't remember ever sharing the crosscut saw with my father. The chainsaw wasn't even a gleam in the inventor's eye at the time whereof I speak.

The theory was simple enough. We cleared enough undergrowth to give us space to work in, then hacked out a chunk of the side of the trunk facing the direction the tree was to fall in. Then we got stuck in with the crosscut saw, one of the best aids to shoulder and upper arm development ever devised. Changing the position of the saw and the use of wedges ensured the tree would fall exactly as planned.

Letting a tree fall in the water was all right in British Columbia. In South Derry it would have led to serious complications for the cutters, the river itself and in all probability, a serious outbreak of bad language. We never let it happen.

Once down, the branches had to be trimmed off — the thicker ones and the trunk cut into manageable lengths for hauling to the saw bench. Our prudent grandfather, when he built his flax mill, thought, 'waste not, want not', and built a saw bench out front, in line with the wheel, so that a belt could be run out to the pulley. The lot was water-powered and environmentally friendly, though if anybody had heard of the environment in his day they thought it was some foreign place.

I was invariably paired off with my oldest brother Brendan for lumberjacking. He was, and remains, a man of few but usually telling words. 'I don't mind you sitting on the end of the crosscut,' he said to me one day as we prepared a trunk for removal to the saw bench, 'just don't trail your feet.'

It's the sort of advice that sticks in your mind, no matter what direction your career takes you.

Calling a Spade a Spade?

'They pelted each other with grapes, is that what you're saying?' said a Welshman to me one time many years ago. 'Why would that end up in court?'

The Rural Community, as Oscar Wilde almost said, is separated from The Rest by a common language. The Welshman was passionately defending the theory that St Patrick came from Wales. I wasn't bothered. I had been taught history by a clergyman called Patrick with two alphabets after his name and he wasn't sure, he told us, whether there were two St Patricks, only one, or none at all. This had led to an angry confrontation with the Welshman who offered to fight me in proof of his assertion.

I said if I hit him with the shovel I was holding I would win and where would that leave St Patrick? I added that billhooks, shovels and graips, occasionally spelt greips, were often used to settle disputes that ended up in Magherafelt Court and it was the last-mentioned agricultural implement that led to his confusion.

The graip, aka greip, is apparently known in polite circles and TV gardening programmes as a fork. I didn't know this myself until I went to buy a graip — sorry, fork — for use in my own garden. Luckily I spotted what I wanted before I was directed to the greengrocer's. My information that, where I came from originally, it was called a graip was met with a glassy stare at the checkout.

The graip was a versatile implement and, apart from its more obvious uses for spreading manure or cleaning out the byre, it could be used to fend off a cross dog and with a foil on the end of each prong, and a slight modification to the design, it was indispensable for shovelling potatoes. Its aggressive uses I have already mentioned. When Lord Byron said of an acquaintance that he was as nice a fellow as ever buckled a swash or cut a throat, he was only paraphrasing the Ballinascreen equivalent, 'He was as nice a fella as ye ever stuck a graip in.'

The Vikings brought us the graip. When visiting friends in Norway I spotted one in their garage. 'Fork,' said Jan helpfully. 'Graip where I come from,' I told him. 'Here, too,' he said delightedly.

As for my own graip, I got half an hour's mileage out of it before it vanished from my suburban garden. An opportunistic urbanite who may not have known the right name for it certainly knew how to get one free.

The Turf-Shed

Central heating dealt a devastating blow to a vital social amenity on the farm. It made the turf-shed redundant. The turf-shed was much more than a simple fuel store. It had an even bigger role than being a place to park the carts, or the tractor, later on, even though both had to be kept dry — the carts because they were wooden and the tractor because nobody wanted to absent-mindedly sit in a puddle of water, a source of haemorrhoidal problems according to the wisdom of the time.

The scythe hung there, of course, and the sharpening stone on the wall-plate conveniently close; and in the rafters swallows built their nests and flew to and fro unhindered, for one side of the structure was open to the elements.

Turf-sheds were close to the road, handy for passing pedestrians and cyclists caught out in a seasonal or unseasonal downpour. There they might find others similarly inconvenienced, or the farmer himself or some of the family, studying the hypnotic effect of the rain dripping off the corrugated roof.

The attraction was subtly psychological. A shed full of turf represented the tip of an iceberg of hard work and, like the man in *Catch-22* who thrilled to the idea of work that called for no effort on his part, there was a certain satisfaction in being close to the efforts of others.

Ceiliers going home were accompanied to the shed-corner, because it had a confessional dimension that was absent elsewhere. Advice was sought or offered; bits of inside, confidential information exchanged about land that might be coming on the market for sale or letting; things that couldn't be mentioned in the wider stage of the farmhouse kitchen.

I hadn't fully appreciated the significance of the

turf-shed until the subject came up in conversation with my cousin Pat, who emigrated to New York in the 1940s, and he recalled the plotting and scheming about getting to dances that he and my older brothers used to indulge in there, safe from the disapproving ears of the older generation.

Then he spoke of my father's brother Vincent, also living in upstate New York, who, with his ten brothers and sisters and their parents had occupied the same house five of us lived in. The turf-shed was vital not only for the exchange of confidences, but the making and remaking of the alliances inevitable in a big family. When my cousin would visit him and the uncle had something confidential to impart, even though he had a big house and only four people in it, he would take him out to the garage.

'It was his turf-shed,' Pat told me. 'It was a genetic thing.' It certainly was.

Farmyards Now and Then

The most expensive pair of shoes I ever bought sprang a leak after a month — 28 days to be exact — so I hotfooted it back to the shop, in a manner of speaking, and a smart-alecky-type salesman viewed me and my deficient purchase with amused contempt.

'You've been walking through a farmyard wearing these,' says he, 'and you've dried them on a radiator.'

He delivered this diagnosis with all the confidence of Sherlock Holmes telling an admiring Watson that the shadowy figure who had just brushed past them in the Victorian fog is a left-handed sagger-maker's bottom knocker with a red-haired, vegetarian widowed aunt living in Bognor

Regis. And, there is such an operative as a sagger-maker's bottom knocker. They practise their obscure trade in the china industry.

The salesman also added, though I couldn't have cared less, that the makers would charge the shop £24 to resole the soles. There are two ways to deal with a situation like this. One is to argue the toss. The other would probably lead to fisticuffs, the intervention of the police and a sequel in court, as the old-time newspapers used to say.

The shoes had never been near a farmyard. Neither had the salesman. His image of farmyards hadn't progressed much from the days of W F Marshall and the resident of Drumlister who lived in clabber to the knees. He had never opened his eyes as he went out and about, or he would have noticed that farmyards have long been seas of concrete where you could walk with impunity wearing slippers, though to be realistic it wouldn't be a clever thing to do.

He was influenced perhaps by the then current fictional tale of the official who visited an isolated farm, and having struggled up the alder-lined, rutted, briar-tangled lane, came upon the amazing spectacle of a farmer trying to harness a bull to a bogged-down tractor in a corner of the swamp that passed for a yard. The farmer was roaring at the animal, 'G'wan ye brute ye, there's more to farm work than romance.' And that, I have to add, is the edited version.

Back, though, to the shoes and their imaginary farm trip. I sent them back to the factory myself and they were returned, good as new, or so I thought, with no mention of a £24 charge. A month later they sprang another leak. This time I consulted a local shoemaker who repaired them for a trifling £6, which dates the event somewhat, I know.

They've been demoted long ago but they're still intact and I wear them when digging the garden. The shoe-shop, though, is a Chinese restaurant this many a year. There's a moral lurking in there somewhere.

Farm Gate? What Farm Gate?

Every time I hear 'farm gate' as in, for example, 'farm gate price' I get a twinge in the left ankle, just like Pavlov's dogs slavering when they heard a bell ring. Gates weren't a priority in the farm budget half a century ago. The makings of an adequate field gate could be had for the cutting down, hammered together with six-inch nails, and hung on a couple of uprights with any bits of old strapping that came handy to hand. If repair or replacement should ever be called for, sure the material was growing all round.

Most farmyards didn't bother with gates at all. They were open plan generations before that trendy expression was born. A garden gate could easily be the head of an old iron bed, which had the double merit of being both attractive and cheap. The iron gate hung on proper posts was mostly a sign that the farmer was coming up in the world.

There were exceptions and one of them was at the end of a neglected lane near our place. Two decaying round pillars flanked a rusting iron gate that was old when the world was young. Two rutted tracks ran on either side of a central ridge of high grass and weeds down past a large tumbledown shed where some local farmers stored their mowing machines, potato diggers and similar equipment during the winter. Beyond the shed we had land taken for grazing and I was often sent to check on the cattle to make sure they hadn't mysteriously multiplied or decreased during the night, or fallen down and broken a leg. The day I was well warned not to take any short cuts was the first time I used the gate. Not for me the athletic vault over. I climbed it rung by rung. At the top I made several instantaneous discoveries. It wasn't attached to anything. The hinges were missing. So was the bar. The thing stood there defying the laws of physics, held upright by the willpower of those deities whose function it is to ambush idiots and provide them with further opportunities for self-destruction.

Then it keeled over, slowly at first but gathering momentum like a Disney cartoon as I flailed wildly in a desperate attempt to learn to fly. When it hit the ground it brought with it most of the skin off one ankle and a somewhat lesser amount of the other. Both feet were firmly trapped. I had failed to learn to fly spontaneously but I had learned another useful skill. Limping on both feet at the same time was both feasible and necessary. The resulting twinges remain with me still.

Having Your Chips

The first time I saw chips was in a shop in Cookstown. I was maybe seven or eight, there was no chip shop in our locality and the nearest thing I ever saw to fast food was a dog haring off up the street with a string of sausages from Johnny McNamee's, the butcher. In the Cookstown incident, it must have been about lunchtime — well, dinnertime in those days — and it seemed a member of the staff had absented himself without leave and gone to get a fish supper.

The shop was crowded and when he came back he was, to put it very politely, told to stop feeding his face and give a hand. Now, I have been around a few corners since then and I've seen many an odd thing, but nothing comes close to the still-lingering sight of that youth putting his fish supper in his trousers pocket. Maybe he thought the crisp instruction to give a hand was just a ploy to get him to put the supper down so that the rest could fall on it, who knows. Maybe he was paraphrasing that ancient wisdom about keeping your friends close and your fish supper closer still, but anyone who has ever brought a fish supper home in the car will know what the motor smells like the next morning. So, what would the trousers be like?

Nothing will ever supplant the chipped potato in the public affection and readers of farming publications will recognise the name of Dr Gama Khan, once charged with the sacred responsibility of finding the perfect chip. The scientific target was the ultimate in sensuousness, a chip crunchy on the outside, soft on the inside, which smelt good, wouldn't become soggy and generally felt right. Who'd be a chip doctor?

Inspiration comes in odd ways. Crisps, first cousin of the chip, were invented in a fit of temper by an American chef called George Crum in 1853, when a guest, in the prestigious Saratoga resort hotel where he worked, kept sending back his fried potatoes demanding they be sliced thinner... and thinner... and thinner. The enraged Crum finally cut them so thin they were transparent, fried them, salted them and delivered them personally. The guest said they were great. Wouldn't we all, with an angry knife-carrying chef breathing down on us? The rest is history. They were in the White House in 1887.

All that research, all that history in the national vegetable... and to think we used to impale them on sharp sticks and hurl them at each other and passers-by. As Marlon Brando remarked in *The Godfather*, young people just got no respect.

Clever Bees

A scientific report issued recently claimed that bees are almost as intelligent as people. I'm inclined to think that it's not much of a tribute to bees, not that I know much about them. Of all the sidelines I recall practised on farms, I don't remember many beehives. Even so, a man who worked around our place on a casual basis mentioned one day at teatime a farm 'down the country' he used to work at where the wife kept a hive or two of bees. 'Down the country' was, like Ireland's mythical fifth province, a mysterious place where the most bizarre things were believed possible and the more unbelievable were probable.

He asked the farmer's wife if the bees had done

well that year. She said they had done fine. They hadn't produced any honey, but she added, with every sign of satisfaction, that they had stung her husband three times. Which is a result of a sort, I suppose. There were others.

At the first hum of the thresher, for example, farmers grabbed their pitchforks and, like the cavalry horses making for the sound of the guns, they made for the source. Threshing meant craic, debating the comparative quality and yield of grain and the ratting skills of farm dogs. Then there was the food.

This was tricky. It had to be plentiful and it was as likely to be talked about as any other aspect of the threshing. Each farm kitchen strove to be different, although you would hardly have thought a dozen farmers bantering each other at the top of their voices would have noticed the menu. The little extra could be as simple as apple tart and custard but even that could be a culinary minefield.

For dessert, one farm wife served large slices of apple tart, baked, as she put it, with a few extras, straight from the recipe book. 'Cut from the book,' amended one diner, for the slices, though generous in size, were painfully thin. She was out of earshot, luckily for all present. Another, desperate for something different, finally settled on a dollop of honey on each side-plate. A good try, tasty, good for health, for energy and, as it turned out, for a sly dig, too.

One farmer, taking advantage of a lull in the banter, a rare thing in itself, twisted his knife round in it once or twice, lifted it six inches or so and mildly remarked, 'I see, Mrs Murphy, that you keep a bee.'

No prisoners were taken at the threshing. Anybody could get stung.

Bread

In 1942 those people charged with the overseeing of the nation's nutrition introduced a thing called the national loaf. The only reference I have ever come across about it stated simply that it was a curious grey colour, but packed with vitamins. That was during the Second World War, of course, when odd things were foisted on the public in the name of nutrition.

During the First World War my father formed certain strong views about foodstuffs, but loaves especially. The family farm didn't need all its sons, so he emigrated to Glasgow, which was a popular destination for young men and women from Ballinascreen seeking a better life. He worked briefly in a bakery, a large establishment with remarkably high standards of hygiene for the time.

The walls and floors were tiled, the bakers wore starched chefs' whites and hats and smoking was strictly forbidden. This was tough in an age when everybody smoked, so the bakers satisfied their nicotine craving by chewing tobacco. This is a foul practice, appealing only to the most hardened of sinners, and apart from the ferocious taste of the stuff it creates the problem of disposal. Even with an asbestos stomach you couldn't swallow tobacco juice but the bakers solved the problem neatly by spitting it into the dough.

From that day on my father distrusted loaves — national, nutritious or otherwise. When he was conscripted soon afterwards he formed the opinion that while army loaves may not have contained tobacco juice they certainly contained sawdust. Since each loaf had to serve seven, though, the amount of sawdust and/or nutrition consumed by any one squaddie was negligible.

When he came back to farm in Drumderg after the war he could at least be sure of what went into the bread. The idea of buying bread would have been met with derision in any farmhouse. Inside every kitchen, or pantry, door stood a ten-stone bag of flour, on a chair usually. Baking was a necessary rite of passage for any farmer's daughter. She might get away with all kinds of inefficiency but if she couldn't bake a decent scone — and do a bit of sewing — her marriage prospects were about nil.

One by one the aunts left home, the grandparents died and one day my father discovered he had to learn to bake for himself or risk goodness knows what in a bought loaf. There was a brief period of toleration when one or other of the aunts baked batches of bread for him but eventually one of them sat him down and said, 'This is how it's done.'

There are no records extant of his culinary skills up to the point when he got married but they were probably negligible. When he was widowed, a few short years later, he resumed his baking and I can truthfully say, from personal experience, he was a much better farmer than a baker.

A Bread and Butter Issue

A Belfast lady once told me she thought nothing of riding her bike to Straw on a Sunday during the war to buy butter. That's a return trip of 100 miles, give or take one or two, and she seemed to think it was worth it, that there was some special merit in the butter. I doubt it. There was Echo margarine in some of it instead, when the grass was poor and the butter pale. One year not so long ago in Normandy the real taste came back to me, when I found that every village inn served the butter in tangy blocks, with the odd spurt of salty water to hit you in the eye as you put your knife in it.

A modern accountant, miraculously transported back to the days of home-produced butter, would briefly observe the operation and pronounce it uneconomic. Such considerations didn't exercise the farmers of those days, or their wives. Their calculations were done in their heads and stayed there, a closely guarded secret forever. The process, though, was labour intensive and worked only because none of the personnel involved put any value on their labour.

Butter production involved milk, crocks, churns, wooden dishes, wooden implements with moulded designs and elbow grease — especially elbow grease — to an amazing degree. The milk was poured through a strainer into the sterile crocks and left to mature under crisp linen covers. Not much elbow grease was required for that, or even for the milking, unless a cow proved cantankerous, which often happened. The physical effort came when the stuff was poured into the sterilised churn, which looks so quaint in a museum, but was anything but when you actually had to work it. When the churn staff was inserted and the lid fitted, the serious stuff began. All that plunging up and down through gallons of milk was excellent basic training for a weight-lifter.

The momentum had to be kept constant and fresh relays were constantly called for, which wasn't all that easy since all the cute folk had departed for the further corners of the land at the merest hint of churning. The end-over-end or revolving churn was somewhat easier to operate and had the added advantage of a tiny porthole in the lid to which tiny specks of butter clung as it formed. The plunge churn had no such device and the operation had to stop for periodic inspections to take place. These set the process back and prolonged the agony.

As for the creative, artistic stuff that so appealed to townsfolk, that was done by the farmer's wife and her wooden paddles and prints and the final product, in hidden costs, probably cost five or six times the price of butter in the shops. However, the labour was free, there were no overheads and by the peculiar economic logic of the time that made it all profit. Then, mercifully, the accountants took a hand in such matters.

The Boiler Suit

Too well I remember boiler suits. They, and overalls, signalled an end of schooling and arrival at man's estate. By some miraculous process you acquired one or other of these and a clapped out bike the day after you left school. You also acquired a job and a licence to smoke, and the whole thing was better than a pools win.

I wanted to get in on the act. My father, with hand firmly on the scruff of my neck and a minimum of words decreed otherwise and my life took a different direction. The opportunity to punch in a twelve hour day for thirty bob a week passed me by, and with it my claim on a boiler suit.

The boiler suit wasn't pressed into service right

away. It was eased into use on Saturday nights in villages up and down the land. No London clubman checking his dinner jacket in a mirror could have been more critical of his appearance than the wearer of a new boiler suit on its first outing.

The top two buttons were open, naturally, to reveal the collar and tie, and the jacket of the Sunday-wakes-weddings-funerals suit was worn on top of that. The Sunday shoes were also worn and they, if they weren't black, were known as yalla. This was the uniform of the transitional rural generation, too old to spend Saturday nights at home listening to the wireless, too young or too broke to go to the pub.

So they foregathered on the corners of the village street and watched the world go by, exchanging banter and routine insults with their peers until the cinema opened its doors in Heron's yard at half past eight and rented them a hard seat for nine pence.

Years ago I bought my first and only boiler suit, hung it on a nail in the garage and wiped one or two paint-brushes on it here and there. There's an old rural saying that if you get the name for early rising you can lie till dinnertime and a boiler suit stained with paint and unidentifiable substances can similarly create an unjustified image of industry. It has had little wear, for it's awkward to get into, out of, too, and restrictive of movement when you're in it.

There was a time, though, when it made a fashion statement and even Churchill was pictured wearing one, pinstriped, of course. That, needless to say, was outside Number 10, not Conville's Corner.

To Cap It All

When I was a youngster I was once sent on an errand to a neighbouring farm. As I neared the house there was a serious discussion in progress, clearly audible over the whole townland. There were no secrets in that house. On a good summer day, it was claimed, they could be heard as far away as the crossroads but this proves very little, for the entire countryside was crisscrossed like a football coupon with road junctions.

By the time I'd got to the door silence had descended, either from lack of breath or ideas. I knocked and stood back, lest perhaps a stray punch or a flying body should come my way when hostilities resumed. The wife came out and I delivered my message. She was in no mood to relay communications.

'He's down with the pigs,' she informed me curtly and pointed in the general direction of the piggeries. When I was halfway down the yard she spoke again.

'He's the one with the hat,' she added in a voice that definitely reached all neighbouring crossroads. Unfair, I thought, but said nothing. That man always wore a cap.

Caps were obligatory on farms. Hats not so. A farmer milking would often jam his head into a nervous or skittish cow's flank, which had either a calming or immobilising effect. That was one role, although a minor one.

Fashion was never a consideration, or even weather protection. For men who got wet through on a regular basis, a wet head or a dose of the sniffles meant nothing. The duncher had a much more important function.

'That lad of yours must be big now,' I once heard a farmer remark to another.

The other man took off his cap, scratched his head, spat and replaced the headgear.

'Dunno,' he said thoughtfully. 'Never saw him standing up.'

The cap here served for emphasis. It gave depth and breadth and weight to the reply. If he had replied immediately the answer would have been a forgettable, throwaway line. The deliberation added by the gesture with the cap guaranteed it a place in folklore.

There's an ancient Irish proverb which translates roughly as, 'If there was work in the bed, he'd lie on the floor.' That has a ring to it all right. It encompasses an entire philosophy, conjures up a clear image of simpler times. It didn't, though, have the emphasis and the personal disappointment conveyed by the removal of the cap, the superfluous head scratching and the careful, thoughtful re-siting of the cap.

Of Barns and Raffles

The social skills required to survive a rural winter used to include singing, dancing, card-playing and mastery of a musical instrument. I came in at the end of that era, though it didn't end with a bang, rather fizzling out over years. It's just as well I wasn't born into the middle of it because I couldn't sing, as a dancer I was — and remain — a danger in traffic, I was an abject failure at cards, and as for the musical instrument, the less said about that the better.

Card-playing skills were exercised under the slightly misleading name of raffles. There was a certain moral ambivalence about card-playing, with its implications of gambling, though it was always understood that no taint applied to card-drives organised for parochial fund-raising. Farmhouses took it in turns to host these Friday night 'raffles', which were either twenty-five or forty-five drives organised on a knockout basis, and the ultimate winner got either a goose or a turkey. This was the proverbial carrying of coals to Newcastle, for every one present had been rearing both types of bird for the Christmas trade, but then it was all about banter and craic and the prize was a minor consideration.

I had never been able to grasp even the simplest moves in card-playing but I had been briefly apprenticed to a local fiddle player, Felix Mullan, even though it was generally accepted by both himself, myself and everybody connected with both of us that I was a musical dyslexic. It was nonetheless a useful, if brief, part of my education, for I accompanied him to play at several barn-dances. I use the term in its original meaning. Barn-dancing came to be used by people who were never nearer a barn-dance than a Boxing Day TV showing of *Seven Brides For Seven Brothers*. The dances whereof I speak were held in barns.

There was no time limit to these Friday night

events. They went on until everybody was too tired to move, throats were too parched to sing, the last scrap of food and drink consumed and the fiddler was a shadow of his former self. My mentor communicated with me about stopping, starting and changing tunes by tapping the side of my shoe with his. He also communicated his displeasure in the same way when I failed to keep up with him though there were times when I had a good excuse.

Once, when I had been noting for future reference the activities of a couple in the hayloft, he kicked the side of my shoe and hissed, 'Mind your playing and pay not attention to them, he's only whispering a wee secret into her mouth.'

Felix, if you're out there somewhere in the cosmos, you were ripped off. I heard Chico Marx pass that line off as his own years later.

Peter Dog One

I had completely forgotten about Peter Dog One until a farmer I was chatting to casually mentioned using a mobile phone. I could see the advantages right away. I recall many a time as a youngster being sent to inform my father that an agricultural inspector, or other official, was waiting for him up at the house and a frustrating business that could be. One of my father's numerous skills was never to be where he was expected to be and always to turn up when I was sneaking an illicit smoke. He also had a low opinion of officialdom, acquired during compulsory military service in the First World War and he was inclined to blame the bearer of bad news for the bad news itself. A mobile phone, had such a thing existed in those dim and distant days, would have placed a safe distance between messenger and message.

Peter Dog One was one of a party of farmers from my part of the world who went to the Balmoral Show one year — a trip that passed into local folklore and was remembered mostly by people who weren't there at all. He wasn't Peter Dog One when they set off, only Tommy, until they stopped at a stand where a salesman was demonstrating walkie-talkie sets, skating neatly over the costs and stressing the advantages of instant communication with the farther-flung reaches of a modern farm.

'Peter Dog One,' says our man, coming out of a Guinness-fuelled daydream and everybody, salesman included, stopped to look in his direction. The salesman enquired if he was interested in the equipment. 'He's not,' said a quick-thinking neighbour. 'His wife's voice will reach the length of any modern farm without it, believe me,' and he piloted him safely out of temptation's way.

'What was all that stuff about Peter Dog One?' he demanded.

‘When I was a young fella,’ Tommy told him, ‘I was out on the mountain one day and there were soldiers from Omagh barracks at target practice along Craigy Pass. They kept me waiting for a good while and every time they sent a message on the radio they’d say “Peter Dog One” first.’

‘I don’t know what they’re putting in the stout at all these days,’ said the neighbour. ‘I’m going to have to keep an eye on you. You’ll buy something you don’t want and can’t afford.’

He was right, too. Well, almost right. The newly-christened Peter Dog One nearly bought a tractor that day too, but the quick-thinking neighbour headed that one off with a surreptitious drinking gesture and a nod in Peter Dog One’s direction. Sufficient unto day is the narrowly-escaped expenditure thereof.

The Social Whirl

There was a farmhouse in Upper Derrynoid where ordinary people would gather of a winter evening and compose poetry, one line at a time from each person until the theme had been fully dealt with. Nobody thought there was anything unusual about this activity or ever knew that that farmhouse kitchen was the last outpost of a bardic tradition that stretched back 2,000 years. The rural community clung to poetry long after city dwellers had surrendered it to the colleges.

The normal ceili-house medium, though, was prose and the topics prosaic, for every winter evening, when the cows had been milked and the cattle fed, people dropped uninvited into each other's houses to tell stories, exchange gossip and advice, to have a bit of a laugh. If it happened nowadays, you'd wonder what they wanted.

If a ceilier had some practical purpose for his visit, he'd drop it in as an afterthought, with his hand on the latch on the way out after a three hour visit. It might be the loan of an implement or maybe something more important, such as the night in one ceili-house, when the last visitor mentioned on the way out that the oul' sister had died that afternoon.

There was a proliferation of elderly bachelors in my childhood, a hangover from the complexities of 19th century landholding, and all of them with a remarkable preoccupation with ghosts. According to them the countryside came alive after dark, if you'll pardon the pun, with ghosts, banshees and unexplained noises from behind hedges. Headless women hanging around the crossroads were a particular favourite, though what had become of their heads and what made the crossroads so attractive was never explained.

I understood things better when I graduated to the status of impish youth and discovered the interesting effects that could be visited on superstitious citizens with torches, jews' harps and borrowed bedsheets.

I remember one ceilier for his cheque book gimmick, for farming was still very much a cash-in-hand activity and a cheque book still had novelty value. He would find some excuse for dropping his on the floor but everybody knew it might represent a pound in the bank or a thousand and pretended they didn't see it. Another affected to never know how many cattle he possessed, to within the nearest dozen, so he regularly announced the result of his latest roundup/head count. Since every man present, if shaken awake at three in the morning, could have given his head count without opening any eye, that usually did get a laugh. He never knew what was so funny. What a pity it all died out before the video camera arrived.

New Lamps for Old

In more sophisticated circles they were known as storm lanterns. In Ballinascreen they were called hurricane lamps, an odd choice of name in a community that had never been nearer a hurricane than a wireless weather report.

They threw very little light on anything but they were, I suppose, better than nothing. In the days before farms had electricity and farmhouses were lit by gas they were the only source of outside illuminations after dark and every farm kitchen had one parked inside the door, lit but turned down low, and ready for either routine or emergency.

Basically a container for paraffin oil with a wick protected by a globe, they were smelly, dangerous and inefficient and the advent of the Tilley lamp was a major step forward in lighting the way to after-dark chores. The Tilley looked pretty much the same as the hurricane lamp, only more solid, and the stopper for the oil-container was a pump which forced the oil in a fine spray up the central stem onto a mantle exactly like a gas-mantle. The stem had to be preheated with a tong-like device soaked in methylated spirits and the mantle wouldn't light until the right temperature had been reached but the result was worth the delay.

The passing of the hurricane lamp was unlamented, though it earned a place in folklore. None of the farmers I knew fished the rivers that bounded their land nor much liked the anglers who did, suspecting them of damaging fences and leaving gates open. One night in the Mountain View Bar a visiting angler was entertaining the assembled congregation with his epic struggle with a fish from the Douglas river. As the tale continued the fish grew in stature until it was the size of Moby Dick.

When he paused for refreshment a listening farmer weighed in with a tale of fishing the same stretch the previous winter, when he too had a titanic struggle with some stubborn creature of the deep. It went on for hours, he said, but he finally landed it.

'And do you know what it was?' he demanded, theatrically. 'It was a hurricane lamp.'

'So what?' snorted the angler. 'There's all kinds of junk in that river.'

'Ah but,' says the farmer, 'this hurricane lamp was lit.'

'I don't believe a word of it,' the angler retorted, 'that's ridiculous.'

'Here's what we'll do,' the farmer suggested. 'You cut three feet off that fish and I'll blow out the lamp.'

Dim, smelly, inefficient though the hurricane lamp was, the Tilley or the 100-watt bulb could never have provided a put-down like that.

Rural Humour

I wouldn't go so far as to say there was a flourishing market in dropped calves in my youth but some people bought them and most of them lived to regret it. These unfortunate animals had an unpredictable lifespan but that didn't stop hopeful but transient — especially transient — salesmen, on their way back to where they came from at the end of a fair day, trying to palm them off on what they hoped were unsuspecting citizens. Any citizen who was unsuspecting where an unknown vendor and a dropped calf were involved had no business in the farming business.

One such improbable farmer was emerging from Pat McCormick's, our local shop, about teatime on a fair day when a van drew up and the driver offered him a bargain calf. They had done business a full year before and the farmer hadn't forgotten.

'I'd buy a dropped calf off you surely,' he said affably, 'only I've left the spade in the moss.'

These two apparently unrelated remarks are readily understandable to any farmer, especially a farmer of, what the French call tactfully, a certain age. But when I once told the story to some city acquaintances, I learned an important lesson. A joke you have to explain is no joke.

The shop where this exchange took place, being a typical country shop of its time, sold everything a farm might need from meal and coal to groceries and odds and ends. All such shops in the old days sold pint or half-pint tin cups, known simply as tins, for use in the fields. They were made by the travelling people, known then as tinkers. A tinker in those politically incorrect days was also a term of abuse for a sharp-tongued person, especially a woman.

During the war, when petrol was scarce, deliveries were made by pony and cart and the son of the house, my cousin Pat, then about 15 and a Western fan, was entrusted with the job. He drove as if it was the Dodge City to Tombstone stage fleeing Indians and when the inevitable crash took place, a shaft was broken and considerable damage done to the cargo, especially some tins for a customer. There was a considerable row when he got home and advised his parents of the disaster.

A few days later, when she judged things had simmered down, a mischief-making woman came into the shop where father and son were working in stony silence.

'How will you get around with the tins, now that the cart's off the road?' she asked, rubbing salt into raw wounds.

'Dunno,' quoth Pat, quick as a flash, 'but don't make any more till we see how it goes.'

Like the man who said to me that the weather was good enough for some of the people using it, that is a tough line to follow.

The Last Sixpence

I grew up in a ceili house, a place where a young person who kept a low profile, with his ears open and his mouth shut, could learn a lot about the simplicities and complexities of rural living. Enormous amounts could be absorbed about peoples' strengths and weaknesses, farming skills or lack of them, card-playing abilities, feuds, alliances, marriage prospects, about the entire characters of a host of people he might never even meet. Or just might ... some day.

There was the litigation and the trespasses that led to it, the jests interpreted as insults, of which Patrick Kavanagh, one of Ireland's foremost poets but a farmer to his fingertips, once remarked, 'Homer made the Trojan Wars of such local rows as these.' This was the stuff of the ceili house. This was where I heard the story of the tracked sixpence, a truly memorable coin.

I'll call the storyteller Matt. His neighbour, let's call him Tom, a man known to be protective about money, had his entire potato crop turned down that year and had to start from scratch with new seed. This was due entirely to his stinginess with fertiliser, according to Matt.

The going rate for a ton of seed that year was £20 and Matt was the only man with any to spare, but it took half a day to get the aggrieved buyer to agree the price.

'He took them away yesterday,' Matt went on. 'I was shaving in the kitchen when he came to pay for them. He threw the three fivers down on the table ready enough, then he started on the pound notes. He put one down and looked at me. I kept on shaving. He put another one down and I thought he would have a weak turn.'

He paused for effect and a silence fell over the group round the fireside.

'Then he produced two ten bob notes, rolled up into wee balls. He smoothed one out, put it down and he looked at me so closely I nearly cut him for I was shaving away. "Keep going, Tom," says I. He gave me the other one. Then he started on the halfcrowns, two bob bits, tanners, threepenny bits. He thought I wasn't counting but there was nineteen pounds, nineteen shillings and sixpence on that table. "You're a tanner short," says I. He threw that tanner down so hard it bounced off the table across the floor. When I picked it up the track of his thumbnail was on it. Here you are, young fella, see for yourself,' and he flicked a sixpence across to me.

There was no mark of any kind on it. I exchanged it for two cones the next day at lunchtime in O'Kane's shop.

Horsepower or Manpower?

I saw a TV programme one time where the researchers had reconstructed an ancient Roman combine harvester and put it to work. I always knew, of course, that they had mowing machines but I thought they were called slaves. This combine was pushed. It consisted basically of an open-fronted wooden box on wheels, the bottom being a set of pointed boards set tight together so that the grain was ripped off and fell into the box.

It looked like seriously hard work, and wasteful, too, for the stalks were left standing, prompting any watching farmers to protest at the waste of bedding, if nothing else. The researchers didn't push too far. They would have had a thin time in the days of the original machines, when the eight hour day was unheard of, you got fed only if you worked and incentive was provided by a whip.

Still, the Romans farmed on a huge scale and excavations in Norfolk revealed that not only had they vehicles for travel as well as work, they also drove on the left, a practice observed more or less to this day, though tractors with a wheel on either side of the white line can be seen on most roads most days. One theory advanced for driving on the left in ancient times was that it left the sword arm free, so that a driver who felt like reaching out and chopping somebody's head off in a fit of ancient road rage could do so unhampered by safety considerations. Happily, this practice has not survived intact into modern times.

We have other ways.

It took 2,000 years for us to use horsepower on the land that didn't actually belong to horses. Slavery didn't officially exist, though that dwindling band of survivors from the hiring fair era could give you an argument about that and they'd be backed up by many a pensioner who worked on the family farm in their youth. The first horsepower on any scale didn't come from the iron-wheeled Fordson but from the Austin 16. With the body stripped off and a tow bar welded on, it could drag a Harrison-McGregor mowing machine with a shortened shaft in a fairly efficient way.

Not for long, though, because the Austin 16 was built to be a taxi and only became a tractor when it was useless on the road. Since we're talking of times many decades before the MOT, their agricultural lifespan was short. When the head gasket blew or the clutch burned out or the bearings went, it was pushed into a corner of a field or a gap in the hedge and another bought for a fiver or so. It was enough to make a horse laugh.

Sauce for the Goose

Many years ago in our parish a woman who reared geese decided the time had come to improve the strain, so she walked all the way to a farm ten miles distant where there was a sturdy species of gander for sale. She did a deal but getting the gander home was a problem. She hadn't thought that far ahead.

She considered the dilemma in a country pub and imbibed a bottle or three of stout, a delicacy for which she had a decided weakness. About the fourth bottle a charabanc driven by a neighbour stopped outside. She wondered if she and the gander could have a lift. No problem, said the neighbour, sure the charabanc is half empty, just take a back seat, and keep that brute under control.

So off they went, the gander, legs tied, in a sack and in a half-nelson under her arm, but with the motion of the vehicle and the bottles of stout she nodded off, the gander slipped its moorings and took a turn up here and there, spreading consternation among the tourists. It got under the seats and the driver pulled over to wake her up and tell her to round up the livestock. Red-faced, she got down on hands and knees but the gas from four bottles of stout wouldn't be denied and issued from her nether regions with a loud report.

'Like your style, ma'am,' said one of the tourists. 'If you can't catch it, shoot it.'

Getting new feathered stock home was often dramatic. When my Aunt Mary's sole post-Christmas laying turkey died on the nest, a quick replacement had to be found. The only one available had to be fetched from Loughry College at Cookstown. Her brother-in-law, whose van and business took him all over the place, was recruited. He put the trussed up turkey in the back of the open van, stopped in Cookstown to do some business and the turkey managed to get out over the tailboard and hobble into a drapery shop which emptied at once.

Then it took a turn under a market stall or two and, by the time the ever-growing posse had rounded it up, there was a trail of broken crockery halfway along the street. When it was finally delivered my aunt said, 'Had you any problems getting it home?'

'None,' said the brother-in-law, 'sure it was only a day's outing.'

I think he meant for the turkey.

As Sure as Eggs

A man I know runs a snack bar in Belfast city centre. One morning a customer came in and, having made sure he had everybody's attention, asked for half a dozen ganders' eggs. He was duly served six hard-boiled standard eggs to take away. Another diner enquired if ganders' eggs were good for you. 'Put hairs on your chest,' the owner assured him, so he too departed with half a dozen standard hard-boiled eggs.

He had a query next morning. 'How come the eggs came hard-boiled?' 'Because,' said the owner of the eatery without a blush, 'a gander is a big bird with a very high body temperature. The egg is formed at the front of the bird and by the time it comes out the other end it's hard-boiled.' The customer departed satisfied, with another half dozen standard eggs.

He was back the next morning with a complaint. Somebody in work told him ganders didn't lay eggs. What was the game? The snackery owner inspected the returned eggs and apologised. Quite right, he said, they were drakes' eggs. And three pence each dearer.

That takes me back to when the laying hen was a power in the land, and the duck and the goose, too. It takes me back to the hiding my cousin Finbarr got for attempting to drown a hen because he had misunderstood a school lesson and formed the belief that when people are drowning they hear sweet music. He had the hen's head and one of his own ears under the water listening — purely in the interests of science — when his mother caught him and administered summary justice.

It also takes me back to ads on the back cover of *The Farmer's Journal* for delph eggs and sunglasses. Delph eggs were placed in the nests to discourage hens from laying away in the hedges and the sunglasses were really wrap around plastic blindfolds to discourage them from pecking the shells of their own eggs. In reality it would have been a remarkably thick hen that would have been fooled by either.

Hens 'laid away', as the expression put it, no matter what precautions were taken in those free-range days. In their tiny minds their eggs were the next generation of hens but in reality they ended up sold, boiled, fried, scrambled, poached or in a cake. So they rebelled, they laid out in the hedges, and farmers' wives would pay a reward for information leading to the discovery of those nests.

We discovered an incredible number of these nests after school in the summer lanes of our childhood. The number was incredible because we occasionally fabricated them ourselves and furnished them with eggs from perfectly respectable sources. The loot from real discoveries was occasionally split up and distributed over other handmade nests and maybe the results reported to several different farms. We were so smart I've often wondered why we didn't end up rich — like the vendor of drakes' eggs masquerading as ganders' produce.

Duck!

A friend told me one day about being slowed to a crawl by a swan that was walking along the white line of a busy thoroughfare. It was maybe not the smartest thing that the swan ever did, especially given the casual savagery that passes for driving in this country, but it did have the right of way. It had a minder without whom it might have discovered something the rest of us have known for a long time. The cemeteries of this land are full of people who had the right of way.

Ducks enjoy the same privilege but hens, indecisive, scatterbrained creatures, don't enjoy legal protection, being likely to change their minds halfway across. It's a moot point. When I was nine or ten, a hen ran out in front of me as I shot past a farm gate in Crieve on my bike, thrust her neck into the front spokes and was neatly beheaded. I was hurled over the handlebars and ended up standing on my head, more or less, in a convenient ditch.

As I counted the stars in this undignified position I was sternly upbraided by an angry farmer's wife magnificently oblivious to my injuries. She seemed to think I had deliberately staged this painful exercise just to decapitate her hen, a creature apparently so prolific she would have put the golden goose in the ha'penny place. The owner demanded compensation in full before I even got my feet back on the ground.

Youngsters of my generation didn't go about the countryside with the price of a hen — or anything else much — in their pockets. I said I would take the matter up with my father as soon as I got home. Or if I got home, for there was an element of doubt about my escape at that point. Of course I never mentioned the subject to him. He was not a humorous man but the very idea would have given him a good laugh.

I fared better than a school contemporary who absent-mindedly slid into the driving seat of a van whose driver he was supposed to be helping and drove off. The roads and lanes weren't crowded in those days and he had been driving vans and tractors with or without their owners' consent from the age of eight. The only casualty of his escapade was a duck which maintained its single-minded way across the road and paid for the exercise of its right of way with its life.

By the time he got home — there was a lengthy discussion with the van-owner to be allowed for — the duck's owner had got there first with her story and departed fully compensated. That day came to a memorably painful end for him, too.

The Labourer is Worthy of His Hire?

When I first heard of a farmer whose son said he was paying him £300 a week I said nothing, but I assumed the father must own at least a county. My first student landlord had been a farm labourer for his uncle in the long ago and he told me of his astonishment at hearing from his contemporaries that they got money for their efforts — occasionally. He tackled the uncle who after a long and vigorous protest finally said, 'All right, I'll give you sixpence.'

'Was that sixpence an hour, a day, or a week, or what?' I asked.

'Just sixpence,' the landlord told me. So he offered the uncle some coarse suggestions about what he could do with his sixpence and went off and joined the army, where he was rather better paid and not worked so hard, though he had the counter-balancing experience of being shot at by bad-tempered foreigners for a couple of years. Afterwards he kept his military moustache and became a successful wholesaler. The experience had hardened him.

It was an almost sacred tradition in Irish farming that fathers and uncles developed wages amnesia. The renowned Frank O'Connor in his travel book *Irish Miles* devoted a couple of pages to the antics of a father and son in a café, on a market day in the 1940s. At the end of their lunch of soup and bread the father takes a two-shilling piece out of a big cloth purse and sends the son, a stripling of about 35, to pay for it. There's change. The son stands looking at the coins. The father ignores him. O'Connor watches them both. Clearly the son wants to keep the change, maybe to buy a packet of cigarettes. The father knows that but makes no move, no gesture. Finally the young man hands over the money and, without a word, the father carefully stows the change in the big cloth purse and they go, the father first, the son following. The titanic, wordless struggle leaves O'Connor exhausted, and he was only watching.

One Draperstown fair day an old-time farmer passed into folklore when he gave his hard-worked adolescent son a shilling. The legend doesn't specify whether he did so willingly or under duress, but there was consternation later when the youth informed him that he had lost it. The old boy's relief when the missing coin turned up stopped well short of the hooley thrown by the woman in the parable when her lost coin was found but his comment, 'Many's the scare ye gave me,' clearly indicated one thing. Just like O'Connor's old farmer, he didn't want the money going out of the family.

Rustling

I remember most farmers having a brand, the size of a poker with a rectangular fitting at one end about the size of a matchbox, bigger maybe, depending on the expertise of the blacksmith. Inspection would show the end of this fitting to be in the shape of the owner's initials. Heated till red-hot, it was used to burn the initials into all newly purchased spades, shovels, forks, rakes, indeed all tools. Tools had a tendency to go walkabout from open sheds and outbuildings and the brand was a deterrent to the activities of the evilly-disposed.

Branding was more commonly associated, in youthful minds, with the cowboy skills of roping and throwing in Western films and especially with that time honoured theme of cattle rustling. We had no real equivalent of rustling, but we did, though, have a Ballinascreen equivalent of horse thievery. Bikes. By the 1940s most farmers hadn't progressed beyond this humble but vital means of transport. Bicycles also attracted the attention of the light-fingered.

Sometimes the thieves only took the pump but more often they took the saddle, a more practical item altogether. Wartime saddles were covered with a species of rexine, which frayed quickly and made the springs a source of discomfort. The post-war arrival of the sturdy leather saddle brought a crime wave into the countryside. They were often stolen.

Sometimes a particularly sadistic thief would leave the stem of the saddle and would no doubt enjoy, from a suitable vantage point, the yelps of his victim, blissfully unaware of the altered seating arrangement, emerging from the pub at closing time, mounting his machine and sitting down on the stem.

More often the whole bike was taken. Bicycle theft occupied much the same place in local folklore as horse thievery in the Wild West and the penalties were similarly enforced on a do-it-yourself basis. One of our neighbours lost his bike in this way but one day he saw it outside a shop as he passed on the bus, so he got off and stole it back.

If he was looking forward to regaling us with his cuteness, he was to be disappointed. As he rode triumphantly into his yard the thief was waiting for him. An exchange of abuse developed into a brawl in which the lawful owner came second, and as he licked his wounds against the turf-shed wall, the usurper produced a spanner, removed the saddle, turned the bike upside down and shook out of the frame a piece of paper with his own name and address on it.

He was a successful rustler. He had changed the brand, you see.

Thatching

Nothing is sacred, nothing is protected from the inexorable onward march of market forces. You would never have thought that Juncus Jancaceae (don't try saying this aloud, it could result in oral injury), from time immemorial the bane of farmers' lives, would become a commercial issue. It seems, though, that our humble rushes are declining in quality, if not exactly in quantity, and can't compete with the superior products of Poland, Hungary and even Turkey.

You didn't think you'd live to see the day we'd be importing rushes. The stuff that was used years ago to thatch cornstacks. Houses, too. Mowed with a scythe, because it grew in such boggy ground you daren't put a mower on it, even if you were prepared to risk a blade, tied in bundles and hauled home to be fashioned into bands for tying flax, bands so tough that even fourteen days and nights in a flax dam hardly softened them.

Rushes, the stuff of legend. Weary travellers in Irish folk tales, arriving at isolated cabins at dead of night, were given a bed of rushes to spend the night on — a few bundles scattered on the floor near the embers of the fire. Invariably these travellers showed their gratitude in the morning by bestowing on their hosts some magical gift, or reward, which caused cynical children like myself to wonder, though not out loud, if they were that smart, why couldn't they have organised better accommodation for themselves?

They were the insulation of potato pits, which with splendid Irish logic weren't pits at all, but above ground, though they had been real pits in the beginning. The rushes, though, with a thick covering of clay, kept the potato crops of old fresh for months in the days before the proliferation of farm buildings provided ample storage.

They didn't, however, portend well of the ground

they grew on. As a teenage schoolboy I once formed part of a squad recruited and supervised by a teacher to dig and lay drains on the school pitch. The teacher had recruited us on the basis that being farmers' sons we would understand the principles of drainage. We didn't disabuse him of his notion. We didn't tell him that when Ballinascreen farmers wanted drains made they hired somebody to do it for them, and paid them out of the government grant provided for the purpose. Digging the drains kept us from the more boring pursuits in the classroom for a while.

My Aunt Maggie quizzed me on the project and was suitably impressed when I described the maths teacher's scientific approach to the drainage question. She invited my Uncle Barney, who was stoically consuming his dinner, to comment. He merely said, 'I wouldn't have much faith in him through rushes,' and continued to eat.

And now, pollution in our water courses decrees that our rushes aren't even fit for thatching. As my aunt would have said, 'What's the world coming to at all?' Barney's comments would have been unprintable.

Keep it in the Family!

The profession of farm labourer is now practically defunct, but when it existed the work was plentiful, if ill-paid, and there was no shortage of hours. Farmers had a mortal terror of not getting their money's worth and for a century, or more, Irish literature abounded with tales of exploitation. The saving of money often occupied as much thought as the harvest.

Benedict Kiely recounts an incident about a man who had the name of being the meanest farmer in Tyrone. His worker approached him one day to ask for a smear of jam on the otherwise dry bread. The man demanded that the worker recite the Lord's Prayer. When he got to 'Give us this day our daily bread,' the farmer snapped triumphantly, 'There you are, damn the word it says about jam.' Request denied. The same man's pet goat followed him everywhere. When the farmer dropped dead one day, the goat also died within the hour. When Kiely senior heard the news he remarked drily, 'It's a pity the goat hadn't lived, he would have got the place.'

The succession, as much as thrift, preoccupied landowners and occasionally the two themes could be combined. A widowed South Derry man had two daughters, more decorative than useful about the place but this didn't bother him and he and an efficient labourer shared the work between them. The labourer was paid the going rate.

The seasons came and went and he could have had no inkling or idea of the curious hand the agricultural gods were about to deal him.

The farmer died suddenly. The land, the workings of which were a complete mystery, passed into the hands of the daughters, who understood perfectly both sides of a pound note. One of them married the farmhand.

In one ingenious move they took him off the

payroll and retained his services. This thrifty action attracted a certain amount of ribald comment among the farming community. The poor fellow's discomfiture wasn't eased by their habit of prefixing statements with 'Before we married John.'

This may have set a trend. Two middle-aged Ballinascreen bachelor brothers engaged a housekeeper, which is the Sunday word for a skivvy, in the time whereof I speak. They too did the sums and one of them married her. At some subsequent time the other one made, shall we say, certain approaches to her and was instantly rebuffed. He was ill-pleased. 'What do you think we married you for?' he demanded.

Romance has departed entirely from the modern agricultural industry.

Gathering in the ... Sheaves?

Three things I remember gathering, four if you count the blackberries, but I ate most of those as I went along, so they don't count. Gooseberries were a cash crop and I was often pressed into service to help my aunt to harvest hers. Consumption of the crop was forbidden because it ate into the profits, but I needed little discouragement. When you waken in the middle of the night clutching your stomach, and wishing for an early death, you know not to do it again, however furtively.

The bushes were probably sprayed with pesticide which was washed off when they reached the jam factory. Whatever the deterrent, it was as nothing to the thorns on the bush which stripped the flesh from unwary hands, if the attention wandered. I remember that in certain select hands the gooseberry thorns were used to cure a sty on the human eyelid, the only constructive use I ever heard for them.

Then there were the blackcurrants. The bushes were no problem but the minty smell of the leaves drew wasps like a magnet, and they resented the human presence. The prohibition about eating the harvest applied here, too, but the berries were too small and tangy to attract anyone other than the masochist.

Most demanding was the gathering of potatoes. With the gooseberries and the blackcurrants you could sit on a stool. With the spuds you inched along like a mobile question mark and you soon learned that to straighten your back was a mistake, for it made bending down again a painful business. Moments of light relief could be achieved by impaling potatoes on sharpened sticks which enabled you to hurl them great distances to the detriment of innocent persons going about their lawful occasions.

This practice was actively discouraged, not because of risk to third parties, but because, like the gooseberries and the blackcurrants, potatoes were a cash crop, a significant cash crop and if hurled around for amusement were money down the drain.

Years later, when I came to study anatomy and physiology, a clinical tutor transported me back in imagination to the potato harvest when he explained that, alone among the animals, man suffered from back problems because he had evolved too quickly from four feet to two. Many years after that again I mentioned this to a man who turned out to be a raging fundamentalist outraged at the suggestion that man wasn't made in the image of God, white, upright and bearded.

I let him ramble on. After all, I thought, the nearest he'd ever been to a potato field was a bag of oven chips.

Gold in Them Thar Hills

When I was a youngster, and probably for decades before, every so often the newspapers would carry a headline about gold in the Moyola. It wasn't news to those who farmed and lived along the riverbank because every time the river rose in flood and then subsided, apart from wreaking havoc to the crops in the low-lying holms, it left streaks of gold here and there on the gravel.

The first time Jim Gunn, our teacher and a keen angler, mentioned the gold, those of us whose way home took us over the Big Bridge went down to see it. There wasn't enough of it to cover a sixpence and the two donkeys in the nearby field refused to be pack mules in our brief fantasy world of ambushes and claim-jumping. We went on home.

Fish were more interesting. No farmer fished the river but visitors did. So long as they used rod and line, and closed all gates behind them, nobody bothered. What aroused local ire were the quick-kill operators who dropped a bag of lime in the water, killed every form of life in it, took the biggest fish and scarpered.

Our area attracted Scottish visitors who stayed in the local farmhouses and were anglers to a man. There was a local custom that, on one evening of their holiday, everybody along the riverbank should turn out and ensure the visitors a good haul of fish, especially if rod and line hadn't been too effective.

The method was to stretch a length of chicken wire underwater from bank to bank while others armed with poles poked about under the bank and drove the fish to the wire where they were caught by hand. Only the biggest were kept. The rest stayed in the water. My abiding memory is of Pat McNeill, who disdained waders and simply walked into the waist-deep water fully clothed, his only concession to dampness being to ask me to mind his chewing tobacco.

For all the ethics of fishing, people had an ambivalent attitude towards the river and thought nothing of dumping all manner of junk in it. The theory, I suppose, was that it would be washed away downstream eventually and become somebody else's problem. We had NIMBYs in those days, too. Of course, like the man who waded in fully clothed, hygiene and allied matters weren't macho concerns.

There's an American Civil War movie which opens with a row between a commanding officer and the regimental surgeon who can't persuade him, or anybody else, to draw the water for the coffee upstream from where horses are being watered. That brings me back to the rivers of my youth, I can tell you.

The Fox Runs Long ...

I sat on a ledge high in the Sperrins one day, scanning the countryside stretched below through my binoculars and I saw a pair of foxes gracefully glide towards the farms of Dunlogan, as silent as the shadow of a cloud. I had no need to wonder what sort of reception they might meet if they were spotted. Foxes were never welcome on any farm.

We had a dog one time, a sturdy animal with a touch of collie in him, an industrious and hardworking cattle dog, but he had the misfortune to have the markings of a fox, although he was bigger and broader in every way. Everybody in the district knew Towser.

For all his reliability and efficiency, a dog's gotta do

what a dog's gotta do, and Towser went walkabout once or twice a year. He'd be gone for days, but after the first day or two anxiety would set in around the farmhouse. Maybe he had had an accident? Maybe he'd been caught in a trap? Indulgent amusement would turn to gathering anger. Why wouldn't he come home and behave himself?

Underneath all the anxiety lay the realisation that good dogs were hard to replace. Of course he'd come wearily home eventually and sleep it off. He was bleeding from one haunch one time and we knew he'd wandered beyond the neighbourhood where everybody knew him and some farmer, mistaking him for a fox, had taken a shot at him. He recovered and the experience didn't cure his wanderlust.

Foxes were a problem in those days, when every farm had hens and chickens and commercially viable egg production. The word that foxes had been seen on this farm, or that, spread alarm, spurred precautionary measures and the hunting began. It was labour intensive and inefficient, though less so than the ludicrous practice of people in fancy dress on horseback thundering across country allegedly in the interests of curbing the fox population. We were spared the spectacle of the unspeakable in pursuit of the uneatable in Ballinascreen.

The pair of foxes I spotted must have belonged to a dwindling population in the mountain forestry. Now foxes, like people, are drifting to the towns, living in gardens, raiding bins, eating cat food, dog food, anything at all, they're not fussy. They never were, of course, and chickens were victims mostly because they were a handy takeaway meal.

The majority of our fox population in those days operated from secure bases in the forestry and the Ministry of Agriculture, ever anxious to keep on good terms with their neighbours, went about curbing them in a scientific fashion. They appointed a trapper, for that was indeed his title, and the need for amateurish efforts on individual farms disappeared. He was a popular man, both professionally and personally, and nobody thought it the least inappropriate, in his line of work, that his name was George Wolfe.

Summertime — and the Duties were Easy

On the Victorian principle that the devil finds work for idle hands to do, the summer holidays for farm children in Ballinascreen marked the availability of fresh labour, free and fulltime. There were blackcurrants and gooseberries to be picked, for a start, and they drew wasps and bees like a magnet. The theory was if you didn't bother the bees and the wasps, they wouldn't bother you. This should have been explained to the insects, not to us.

The hazard with the gooseberries was thorns. In the right hands the thorns from a gooseberry bush allegedly had healing properties. They were often in my right hand, the left too, but they cured me of nothing, especially not the desire to be somewhere else.

Many years later I would learn from a textbook by a distinguished Irish doctor that nearly all country cures, gooseberry thorns included, had been the conventional medicine of ancient times. The accompanying rituals had been added later to lend an aura of magic. A boy in my class in Draperstown school claimed to be the seventh son of a seventh son and therefore qualified to cure warts — so one last day of school we found him one, and demanded proof.

He did his best but it wasn't good enough. He spat on it, he rubbed dirt on it, he even blessed it but it just sat there unmoved. The mob was about to turn ugly and stone the prophet out of town when Master Gunn showed up, like the cavalry in the last reel, and explained that he was the seventh child, not the seventh son, so we went home without having cast any stones and joined the farm work force. I'm still not sure what magical powers seventh sons of seventh sons possess.

Under the heading of light duties there also came driving cattle to water, because not all grazing was on the banks of convenient summer streams, and checking them on a regular basis to ensure that they didn't find the corn on the other side of the hedge juicier than their own rations. Clegs often made the other side of the hedge more attractive. A bullock with a cleg in his bonnet wouldn't let a trifle like a hedge slow him down.

We had the possibility of more interesting experiences, of course. I had my first driving experience at the age of eight when I steered Stanley Drennan's Fordson tractor between the rows of flax-beets, while he, and his brother George, forked them onto the trailer. There's a whole raft of legislation, European and local, against such joys nowadays. I'll never forget the surge of power as I hauled the wheel round and set off down the next two rows. The tractor was pretty powerful too.

Money for Old Rope

I bought a length of rope one day and discovered many things. If I had asked for a specified length I might have seen it being cut and learned something useful. As it was, I just bought what was left on the drum and found that it didn't so much cut with the Stanley knife as unravel. I also found that my skill at knotting had deserted me and resulting efforts at tying things down looked decidedly unreliable. Having once had a load of stuff blow off my roof rack on the M1, I looked at the length of blue rope and hung it back on the nail on the garage wall plate. If I keep things long enough they may turn out to be useful, although I don't usually make this discovery until the day after I throw them out.

A rope salesman used to turn up at the June fair in Draperstown long ago. His sales pitch included stripping to the waist and going through a series of contortions which, he claimed, would make his torso twice its normal size. It made no change in his dimensions that I could see but it drew a good-humoured, wisecracking crowd and people in good form are more likely to put their hands in their pockets than not.

He sold three thicknesses of rope. Light, but coarse, stuff for thatching cornstacks, a heavier smoother variety for leading an animal and a type heavy enough to moor a small ship but which was used on hay carts. His offbeat sales pitch was rendering a small rural skill obsolete. Every barn on every farm used to have a gadget for making grass ropes.

It was a piece of heavy duty wire shaped like a starting handle with one end twisted into a hook. Two round wooden cylinders were slipped over the wire, one over the short end and one over the middle bit. These were the vital hand grips, for rope making was blister making work, too.

The operator held the long grip in one hand, and

turned with the other, and the second half of the team fed the hay or grass onto the hook. The operator had to walk backwards as the rope lengthened and often provided amusement for his colleague by falling into drains or tipping over rakes. Ropes made in this way were an ecologist's dream because they were biodegradable and rotted back into the ground when they were finished with, unlike my blue abomination which will probably outlast the planet.

Economy, though, and not ecology lay behind the grass ropes. Nobody expanded their holding by squandering money on a would-be Charles Atlas product, when an endless supply of stuff, just as good, grew out of the ground.

Also available by Owen Kelly
from The Brehon Press

ESSENTIAL NORN IRISH

Yer Man's A to Z Guide to Everyday Banter

Are you left not having a baldy by what punters around you are saying? Does the way you hear English being spoke lack rime and raisin? If so, this is exactly the wee toady book you've been duking for.

Self-proclaimed Norn Iron expert Owen Kelly has compiled the definitive basic introduction to local lingo, helping the reader to tell the difference between an "Absolutely!" and a "Wise!" So, whether you're a native or a visitor, and without Annie Furderadoo, overcome your diffs and join in the banter. Square crack!

Praise for Owen Kelly

"An original mind with a refreshing line in humorous understatement." The Times Educational Supplement

"The authentic voice of Ulster — irreverent, independent, humorous and humane." Northern Life

"A fine crack of Flann O'Brien-ish lyrical fancy." The Times Literary Supplement

ISBN 1 905474 00 8 £3.99 paperback